DENNIS & GNASHER SKULL SPINNING PUZZLES

BEANO books
geddes & grosset

WATCH OUT FOR SURPRISES FROM BERYL THE PERIL! TRY TO SPELL AT LEAST 20 WORDS OF FOUR LETTERS OR MORE FROM THOSE FOUND IN —

PLUM IS SURE TO SCORE UM BULL'S-EYE ON UM TARGET IF YOU LEAD HIM TO ITS MAZEY MIDDLE!

NAME THE COUNTRIES BILLY WHIZZ HAS BEEN TO, BY UNSCRAMBLING THEIR NAMES ON THE SIGNPOST.

FILL IN THE ANSWERS TO THE CLUES GIVEN, READING ACROSS, TO GIVE THE FIRST NAME OF THE "PUZZLE" CHUM READING DIAGONALLY DOWNWARDS IN THE DIRECTION OF THE ARROW.

1. Riches.
2. Glass opening in a wall.
3. Stroll aimlessly.
4. A Whelk.
5. Made from a tree.
6. Someone who forms letters with a pen.

	W					
1	W					
2	W					
3	W					
4	W					
5	W					
6	W					

BALL BOY'S FAVOURITE SPORT IS FOOTBALL, OF COURSE, BUT CAN YOU FILL IN THE BLANKS IN THE GRID WITH THE NAMES OF THE OTHER SPORTS HE'S INTERESTED IN?

Answers:— Golf, polo, badminton, basketball, baseball, squash, sailing, athletics.

Answer:—
"Take the rubbish out to the bin and do not wear it!"

HERE'S A SIMPLE PUZZLE FOR "U"! HOW MANY THREE-LETTER WORDS CAN YOU MAKE, WITH "U" AS THE MIDDLE LETTER?

5 to 15 — Think again!
16 to 25 — Could be better.
26 to 35 — Not bad, but not great!
36 to 45 — That's more like it!
46 and over — Well done!

THE NUMSKULL'S LAD'S HEAD IS SPINNING AFTER BEING ON THAT FAIRGROUND RIDE! YOU CAN HELP BY CHANGING SPIN TO STOP IN FOUR MOVES, CHANGING ONE LETTER AT EACH MOVE, FORMING A NEW WORD EACH TIME.

Answer:— Spin, shin, ship, shop, stop is one possible solution.

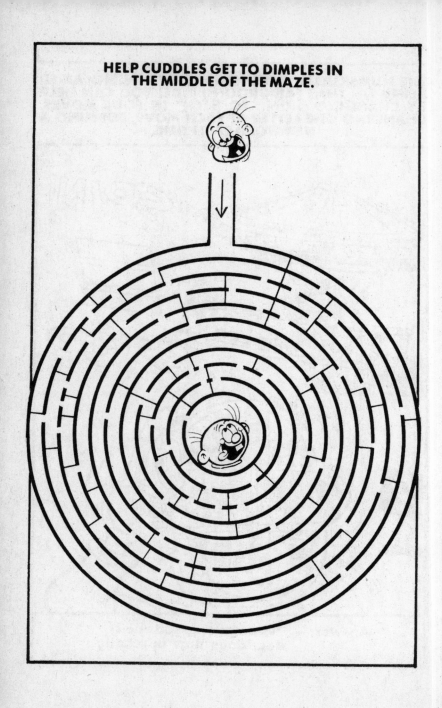

BIFFO IS STUMPED WITH THIS ONE! FILL IN THE GAPS IN THE GRID BELOW TO COMPLETE THE SEQUENCES OF NUMBERS.

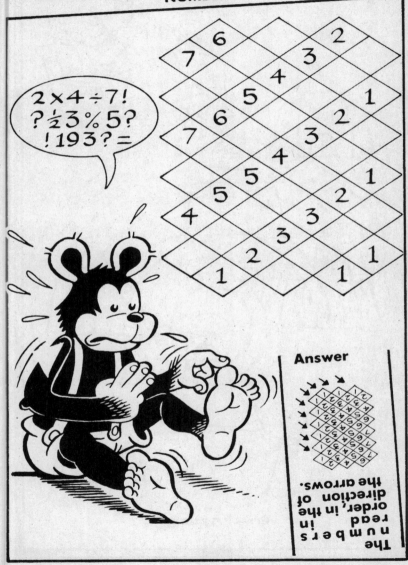

Answer

The numbers read in order, in the direction of the arrows.

SPOT LES PRETEND'S TWO IDENTICAL SANDCASTLES!

Answer:— D and G.

SNITCH AND SNATCH ARE BAFFLED. GIVE THEM A HAND TO PLACE 9 VOWELS CORRECTLY BETWEEN THE LETTERS BELOW SO THAT A 5-WORD SENTENCE IS PRODUCED.

THLNNGTWR
FPS

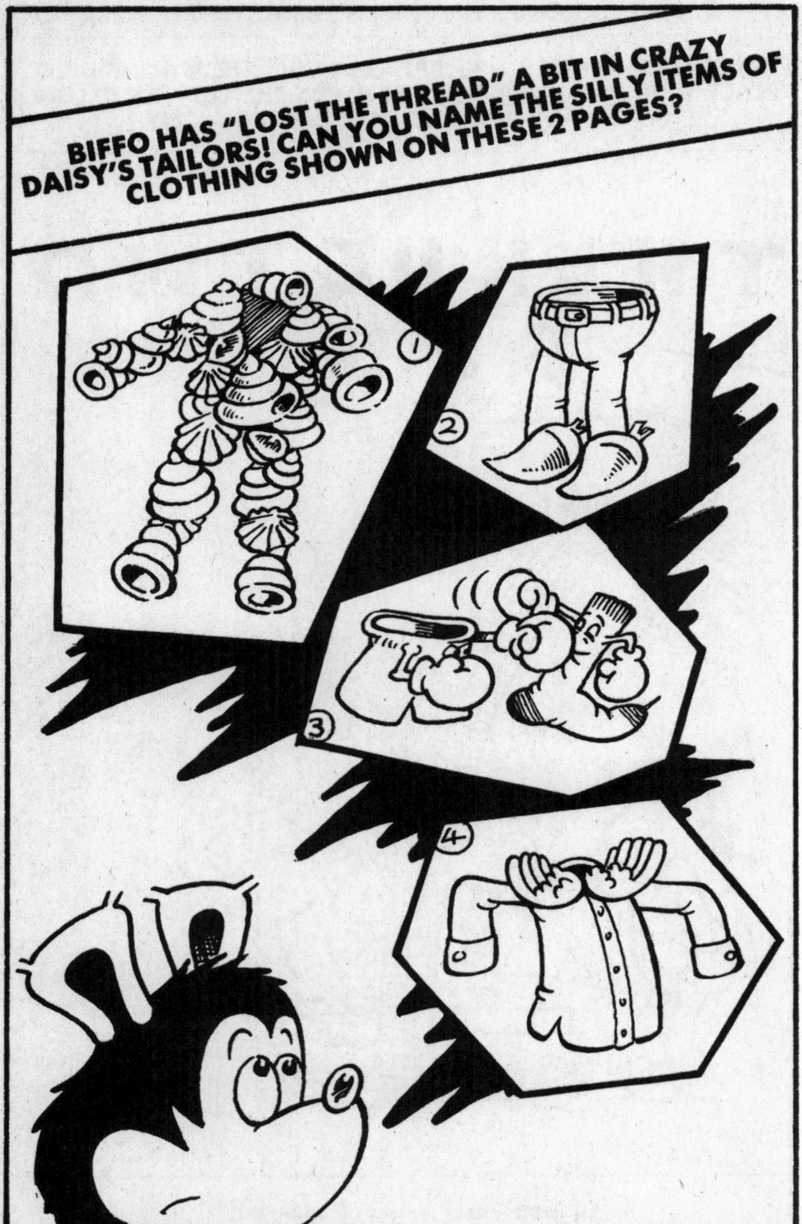

BIFFO HAS "LOST THE THREAD" A BIT IN CRAZY DAISY'S TAILORS! CAN YOU NAME THE SILLY ITEMS OF CLOTHING SHOWN ON THESE 2 PAGES?
1
2
3
4

OH, DEAR! LOOKS LIKE THIS LOT ARE HAVING A REAL ARGUMENT. STARTING AT THE LETTER T AND BY MOVING FROM LETTER TO LETTER IN ANY DIRECTION, SPELL OUT AN APPROPRIATE PROVERB ON THE GRID ON THE LEFT. (YOU'LL HAVE TO USE SOME OF THE LETTERS MORE THAN ONCE.)

N	Y	C	H	B
A	O	T	R	E
M	K	O	I	H
S	S	P	L	T

Answer:— "Too many cooks spoil the broth!"

DENNIS THE MENACE HAS GOT A NEW **CAMERA** TO TAKE WALTER'S PHOTOGRAPH. SEE HOW MANY WORDS OF FOUR LETTERS OR MORE YOU CAN MAKE FROM THE LETTERS IN **CAMERA**.

THIS PUZZLE TAKES A BIT OF THINKING! ANSWER THE CLUES HELD BY THE BASH ST. PUPS TO GIVE YOU A WORD THAT RHYMES WITH A BREED OF DOG!

1. To sketch idly.
2. According to the law.
3. You wear a pair of them on your legs.
4. A game where you have to cover all the numbers on a card.
5. Aunt Aggie's 'posh' name for her desperate nephew!
6. A note sent through the post.
7. A moo-ing animal.
8. A container for pouring liquids.

Answers:— 1. Doodle — poodle — beagle. 2. Legal — schnauzers — dingo. 3. Trousers — schnauzers — dingo. 4. Bingo — Daniel — spaniel. 5. Daniel — spaniel. 6. Letter — setter. 7. Cow — chow. 8. Jug — pug.

LES PRETEND IS IN SEVERAL MINDS ABOUT WHAT OUTFIT TO WEAR AT THE FANCY DRESS PARTY! UN-JUMBLE THE LETTERS ON EACH PACKAGE TO FIND OUT WHAT HIS CHOICES ARE.

1. NOPECLAIM

2. REDOILS

3. TRIPAE

4. CBOOWY

5. MTPAR

6. NOCWL

CAN YOU WORK OUT WHAT THE THREE BEARS HAVE PINCHED FROM HANK'S STORE, FROM THE CLUES ON THE SACK?

Answers:—

1. Mole-asses — molasses.
2. Corn.
3. Blank-et — blanket.
4. C and y — candy.
5. Bl under bus — blunderbus.

CAN YOU PUT THE BALLS THAT BILLY WHIZZ IS JUGGLING, INTO 6 PAIRS, SO THAT THE NUMBERS ADD UP TO THE SAME TOTAL IN EACH PAIR?

Answers:—

8 + 15, 9 + 14, 10 + 13, 7 + 16, 6 + 17, 5 + 18 all equal 23.

WHY IS WALTER "CRACKING UP" SO MUCH? RE-DRAW THE BOXES BELOW, IN THEIR CORRECT ORDER, TO FIND OUT!

Answer

IVY'S DAD NEVER GETS THE NEWSPAPER IN ONE PIECE! SEE HOW MANY COMPLETE WORDS OF FOUR-OR-MORE LETTERS YOU CAN MAKE, USING ONLY THE LETTERS IN "NEWSPAPER". NO PLURALS ALLOWED.

Answers:—

Near, paper, preen, sweep, weep, reap, wean, renew, spear, nape, pane, spare, wear, ware, swear, wasp, wren, swap, span and pear are 20.

WHO'S PHONING WHO? TRACE THE PHONE LINES TO FIND OUT.

FARMER DENNIS HAS JUMBLED-UP THE NAMES OF HIS ANIMALS AND WHAT THEY EAT. SORT 'EM OUT FOR HIM, WILL YOU?

① CRABARBROTIT

② BODOGNE

③ COGRAWSS

④ COCHRICKNEN

⑤ MIBULLDEGITE

⑥ HOOARSTES

Answers:—

1. Rabbit and carrot. 2. Dog and bone. 3. Cow and grass. 4. Chicken and corn. 5. Budgie and millet. 6. Horse and oats.

FOLLOW THE DOTS AND FIND YOUR FAVOURITE FRUIT-FLAVOURED FELLA!

WHICH PATH WILL LEAD ROGER TO HIS MISSING DODGE BOOKS?

1 2 3 4 5 6 7

VOL. 1 VOL. 2 VOL. 3 VOL. 4 VOL. 5 VOL. 6 VOL. 7 VOL. 8

Answer:—
4

WHAT A RACKET! CAN YOU FIND ALL THE INSTRUMENTS, LISTED BELOW, IN THE WORDSQUARE? THEY CAN READ IN ANY DIRECTION, IN A STRAIGHT LINE. IF YOU FIND THEM ALL, THE UNUSED LETTERS WILL SPELL OUT THE NAME OF THE CONDUCTOR!

PIANO, TRIANGLE, TROMBONE,
BASSOON, FRENCH HORN, TRUMPET, DOUBLE BASS,
VIOLIN, PICCOLO, LUTE, HARP, FLUTE, DRUMS, CELLO, BANJO, ACCORDION.

F	D	R	U	M	S	M	P	T	P
R	O	E	L	G	N	A	I	R	T
E	U	B	A	N	J	O	A	U	R
N	B	O	V	P	I	H	N	M	O
C	L	L	N	I	N	I	O	P	M
H	E	L	E	C	O	T	H	E	B
H	B	E	E	C	M	L	I	T	O
O	A	C	C	O	R	D	I	O	N
R	S	N	F	L	U	T	E	N	E
N	S	N	O	O	S	S	A	B	X

Answer:— The unused letters spell "Minnie the Minx"

BALL BOY SUPPORTS **BOTH** OF HIS LOCAL
TEAMS, UNITED AND CITY.
CAN YOU NAME AT LEAST 10
"UNITEDS" AND 10 "CITIES"
IN THE ENGLISH AND
SCOTTISH LEAGUES?

Answers:—

CITIES

Birmingham City, Bradford City, Brechin City,
Bristol City, Cardiff City, Chester City, Coventry City,
Exeter City, Hull City, Leicester City, Lincoln City,
Manchester City, Norwich City, Stoke City, Swansea
City, York City.

UNITEDS

Ayr United, Cambridge United, Carlisle United,
Colchester United, Dundee United, Hartlepool
United, Hereford United, Leeds United, Maidstone
United, Manchester United, Newcastle United,
Oxford United, Peterborough United, Rotherham
United, Scunthorpe United, Sheffield United,
Southend United, Torquay United, West Ham
United.

JOIN THE DOTS TO UNCOVER
THE UGLY URCHIN!

Answers:—

1. A knee — Annie. 2. Car, men — Carmen. 3. Rose.
4. Jack-A — Jacquie. 5. June. 6. Ivy. 7. Car o-line —
Caroline. 8. Beat rice — Beatrice. 9. A net — Annette.
10. Mow — Mo! (Ahem!)

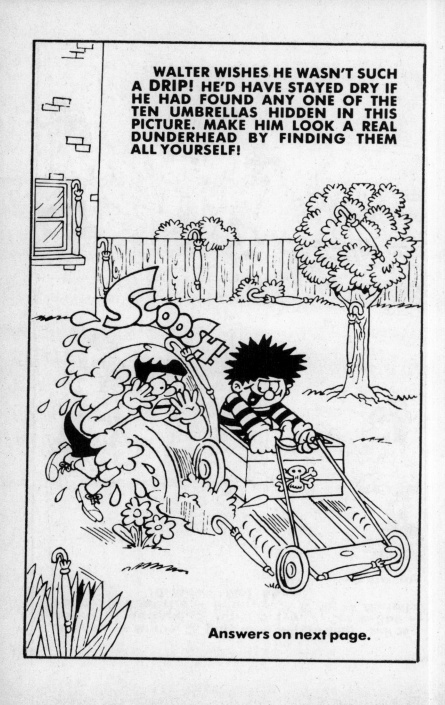

DENNIS THE MENACE THINKS WALTER IS A LOAD OF RUBBISH AND SHOULD BE PUT ON THE **DUST-CART!** SEE IF YOU CAN CHANGE **DUST** TO **CART** IN 6 MOVES, ALTERING ONE LETTER TO FORM A NEW WORD AT EACH MOVE.

DUST

— — — —

— — — —

— — — —

— — — —

CART

Answer:—
Dust, must, mast, cast, case, care, cart is one solution.

SPOT THE 10 DIFFERENCES BETWEEN THESE TWO PICTURES OF A MUSICAL MENACE!

Answers

Dan doesn't know his own strength! You can "win" this puzzle if you fill in the fairground attractions on the grid.

WHAT A STRANGE SENTENCE WALTER'S CHUM, BERTIE, IS YELLING. IN HIS PANIC, HE HAS MIXED-UP FOUR VOWELS IN THE SENTENCE. FIGURE OUT WHICH ONES HE'S MIXED-UP AND SAVE WALTER FROM A NASTY SURPRISE . . . OR MAYBE YOU SHOULDN'T . . . ?

LEEK EIT! DONNUS US BOHUND YEI!

SPOT UM TEN SILLY MISTAKES UM ARTIST HAS MADE TO THIS PICTURE.

Answers:—

1. Wigwam has a chimney. 2. Upside-down wigwam. 3. Christmas tree with snow on it. 4. Wigwam has a front door. 5. Plum riding backwards. 6. Plum wearing a wellie. 7. Cooking pot upside-down. 8. Brave wears a fish-bone in his headband. 9. Cactus has normal, tree-type leaves. 10. Chiefy wears a banana skin instead of a moccasin.

AMAZE YOUR FRIENDS WITH THIS SIMPLE SUM!

Ask a pal to think of any number between one and nine . . . don't let them tell you it!
Ask them to double it,
add four,
halve the result,
then subtract the original number
they thought of.

You can then announce the answer they have is TWO
(this works for any number between 1 and 9.)

SPOT THE TWO MATCHING MICKEY THE MONKEYS!

Answer:—
2 and 4

WINKER WATSON IS OUT OF BOUNDS.
HE IS AT THE SCHOOL **GATE** TRYING
TO REACH HIS **DORM** WITHOUT
MR. CREEP SPOTTING HIM.
HELP WINKER GET IN BY CHANGING
GATE TO **DORM** IN 6 MOVES,
ALTERING ONE LETTER TO FORM A NEW
WORD AT EACH MOVE.

GATE

— — — —

— — — —

— — — —

— — — —

— — — —

DORM

Answer:—

Gate, mate, mare, move, tore, form, dorm is one solution.

POOR DIMPLES DOESN'T KNOW WHICH ONE IS THE REAL CUDDLES! HELP HIM FIND HIM AS HE'S THE ONE THAT'S SLIGHTLY DIFFERENT FROM ALL THE OTHERS.

Answer:—

E — 'Cos that's the one with the dirty fingers!

THIS PUZZLE MIGHT SEEM TO BE SIMPLE, BUT SMIFFY WOULDN'T AGREE. WHAT YOU'VE GOT TO DO IS RE-ARRANGE ALL THE GIVEN NUMBERS, ONE INTO EACH EMPTY SQUARE, SO THAT ALL THE ROWS INDICATED BY THE ARROWS WILL ADD TO 21.

ANSWER:

Fill in the rows across as follows. Row A — 7, 5, 9. Row B — 9, 7, 5. Row C — 5, 9, 7.

SPOT THE 10 ITEMS THAT APPEAR IN BOTH THE PICTURES ON THESE TWO PAGES.

TOP DODGES

Answers

SPOT THE 10 DIFFERENCES BETWEEN THESE TWO "FINE" BASH ST. PHOTOS.

Answers

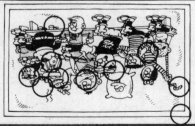

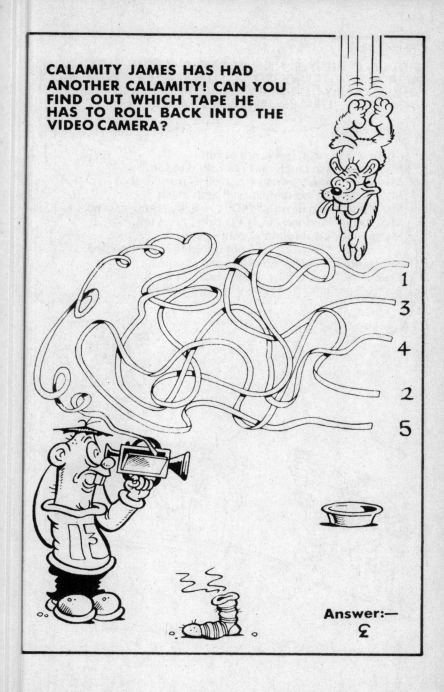

FIDDLE O'DIDDLE HAS ESCAPED FROM MULDOON, AGAIN — THANKS TO A LITTLE HELP FROM BILLY WHIZZ. ARE YOU LUCKY ENOUGH TO FIND THE IRISH ITEM FROM FIDDLE'S RIDDLE?

My first is in rush, but is not in run,
My second is in laugh, but not found in fun.
My third comes from race as well as from dash.
My fourth is in mangle, as well as in mash.
My fifth's found in rush AND in run, this time, as well,
My sixth is Muldoon, and O'Diddle, I can tell.
My seventh's not found in getaway,
                          but it is in the word escape,
My eighth is in joke and not found in jape.
Complete, I'm for luck, if four-leafed I am found,
An Irish emblem that grows in the ground!

Answer:— Shamrock.

CHANGE ONE LETTER OF EACH OF THE WORDS BELOW TO SPELL 6 FISHIES KORKY'S HOPING TO CATCH!

Answers:—

1. Paddock becomes Haddock. 2. Base becomes Bass.
3. Cart becomes Carp. 4. Puppy becomes Guppy.
5. Perth becomes Perch. 6. Saloon becomes Salmon.

DAN IS LOOKING FOR THE MATCHING PAIR OF BARBELLS, SO HE CAN DO SOME ARM EXERCISES. POINT OUT THE PAIR FOR HIM, WILL YOU?

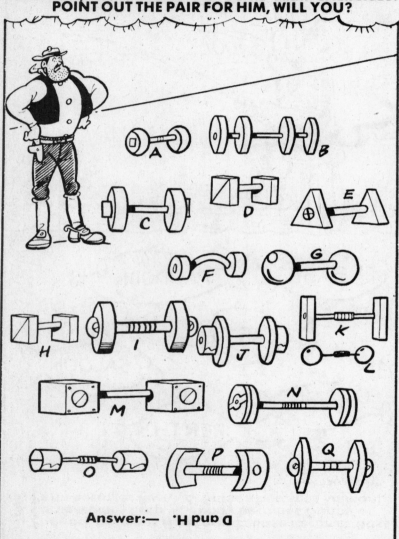

Answer:— D and H.

RE-ARRANGE THE INITIAL LETTERS OF EACH OBJECT BELOW TO SPELL THE NAME OF THE "PUZZLE" CHUM WHO'S SPYING BEHIND ONE OF THEM!

Answer:—

The initial letters of Duck, Igloo, Net, Apple, Holly, Mushroom and Ostrich spell Dinah Mo.

MOLLY DOESN'T EXACTLY SING LIKE A NIGHTINGALE! TO HELP TAKE YOUR MIND OFF THE 'ORRIBLE NOISE, SEE IF YOU CAN FILL IN THE NAMES OF THE BIRDS LISTED BELOW, IN THE CROSSWORD. "NIGHTINGALE" IS IN ITS CORRECT PLACE, AS A START.

NIGHTINGALE, BUDGIE, CANARY, PELICAN, PENGUIN, VULTURE, ROBIN, HERON, RAVEN, BLACKBIRD, OSTRICH, EMU, FINCH, GREBE, CROW, PARROT, OSPREY, WREN, GANNET.

TWEET, YOU STUPID BIRD! TWEET, WILL YOU?

WHICH PIECE OF TILING WILL FIT INTO THE GAP IN SNOOTY'S FLOOR?

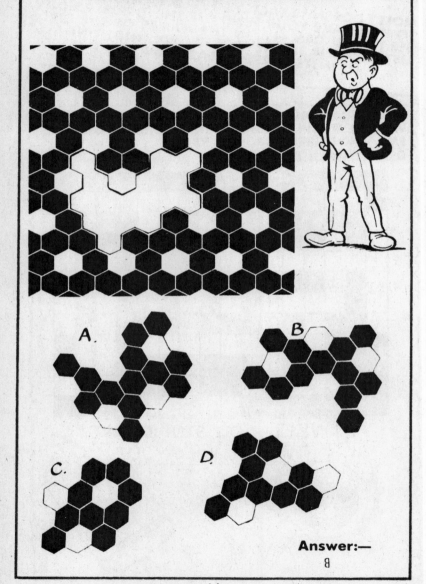

Answer:—

B

MATCH UP THE MIXED-UP PHRASES WITH THEIR CORRECT PICTURE OF IVY THE TERRIBLE!

1. "What makes you think I've used your perming lotion, Mum?"

2. "The water in the swimming pool is FREEZIN'!"

3. "My bed makes a great trampoline!"

4. "'Course I'd be good in the church choir . . . see?"

5. "My bubble-gum bubble burst!"

FATTY FUDGE AND HUNGRY HORACE ARE A REAL PAIR OF GUZZLERS! CAN YOU MATCH UP THE "PAIRS" OF FOOD THEY'RE ALL SET TO SCOFF?

PRUNES

CHIPS

MASH

MILK

EGGS

YORKSHIRE
PUDDING

Answers:—
1. Fish and Chips. 2. Bacon and Eggs. 3. Prunes and Custard. 4. Roast Beef and Yorkshire pudding. 5. Cornflakes and milk. 6. Sausage and Mash.

CAN YOU SPELL AT LEAST 5 TYPES OF WARSHIP, ONLY USING THE LETTERS ON THE SHIP? YOU CAN USE EACH LETTER AS OFTEN AS YOU LIKE.

TEACHER IS AT "WAR" WITH THE BASH STREET KIDS. CAN YOU FILL IN THE EMPTY BOXES TO COMPLETE THE WORDS THAT ALL START WITH THE LETTERS W.A.R.?

Clues:—
(a) Where rabbits live.
(b) Capital of Poland.
(c) A piece of furniture.
(d) To sing like a bird.
(e) A fighting soldier.
(f) An ugly animal.
(g) A prison guard.
(h) A building for storing goods.

THERE ARE 26 LETTERS OF THE ALPHABET ON DENNIS'S COMPUTER KEYBOARD. CAN YOU BE A REAL CLEVER-CLOGS AND MAKE 26 WORDS OF 4-OR-MORE LETTERS, USING ONLY THOSE THAT APPEAR IN "COMPUTER"?

COMPUTER

Answers:—

Perf, come, prom, crop, poem, trump, Rome, mope, rope, cope, tone, mote, term, crept, pour, pout, cute, curf, court, port, mute, puce, rump, romp, tore and pure are 26.

KORKY'S THREE KITS ARE ABOUT TO HAVE A RACE ACROSS THE THREE BRIDGES BELOW. WHO'S GOING TO GET TO THE OTHER SIDE FIRST? HAVE A GUESS BEFORE YOU MEASURE THE THREE BRIDGES!

Answer:—

The three bridges are all the same length, so they'll ALL be first . . . or last, as it were!

BERYL THE PERIL AND MINNIE THE MINX ARE RACING TO GET THEIR WEAPONS. HELP THEM THROUGH THIS DOUBLE-MAZE TO REACH THE WATER-PISTOL AND THE PEA-SHOOTER.

SPOT THE TWO SPORTING SMIFFYS THAT ARE THE SAME FROM THIS SILLY SEVEN!

Answer:— 2 and 7.

CAN YOU SPOT THE DELIBERATE MISTAKE OUR ARTIST HAS MADE IN EACH PICTURE OF THE STORY?

SEE IF YOU CAN SPELL 5 FIVE-LETTER WORDS BY USING THE LETTERS IN "AS LET" TO SPELL EACH WORD.

AS

LET

Answers:—
Tales, stable, least, slate, steal are 5.

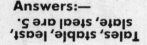

SPOT THE FOURTEEN DELIBERATE MISTAKES OUR ARTIST HAS MADE TO THIS PICTURE.

WHEN YOU WEND YOUR WAY THROUGH THE WICKED WOOD, WATCH WARILY FOR WARLOCKS AND WITCHES!

JONAH IS A REAL MENACE ON THE OPEN SEA! WHILST WE WAIT FOR THE SHIPWRECKED CREW TO BE RESCUED BY THE LIFEBOAT, SEE HOW MANY WORDS OF 5-OR-MORE LETTERS YOU CAN MAKE, USING ONLY THOSE THAT APPEAR IN THE WORD "DISASTER". NO PLURALS ALLOWED.

ARGH! IT'S 'IM!

Answers:—
Raise, aster, trade, staid, sister, stair, stare, sated, raised, stared, resit and resist are 12.

MATCH UP THE SIMILAR SOUNDING PAIRS OF ITEMS ON THESE TWO PAGES.

Hare and hair.   Tale and Tail.   Cent and Scent.   Tee and Tea.   Itch and 'H'.   Ball and bale.   Pier and Peer.

Which of these shadows matches up with Ivy?

Answer:—
D

OOPS! IT'S A BIT **TOO** STORMY FOR IVY THE TERRIBLE!
BRING HER BACK TO EARTH BY CHANGING "WIND"
TO "CALM" IN 5 MOVES, CHANGING ONE LETTER AT
EACH TURN, TO FORM A NEW WORD.

WIND

CALM

Answer:— Wind, wild, will, wall, call,
calm is one soluution.

Answer:—
A black heart and a white bow tie.

THE POSTIE WANTS TO DELIVER A LETTER, BUT HE DOESN'T WANT TO MEET GNASHER! WITHOUT CROSSING A LINE, SEE IF YOU CAN FIND A SAFE ROUTE FOR THE POSTIE! YOU ARE NOT ALLOWED TO TURN BACK.

Answers on next page.

OUR ARTIST HAS MIXED UP ALL THE "PUZZLE" CHUMS' LEGS! SORT THEM OUT FOR HIM, WILL YOU?

Answers:—
5—B
4—A
3—E
2—D
1—C

Answer to previous page:—

1. Bird flying upside-down. 2. Smiffy wearing army helmet instead of cricketer's one. 3. Plug wearing sausages instead of pads. 4. Plug's stumps made out of rhubarb. 5. Danny bowling a dice, not a cricket ball. 6. Plug using baseball bat instead of cricket bat. 7. Danny wearing boxing gloves. 8. Danny's stumps upside-down. 9. Golf hole in the middle of the cricket pitch. 10. Teacher is facing the wrong way to umpire!

HELP DENNIS THE MENACE COMPLETE THE WORDS ON THE RIGHT FROM THE CLUES ON THE LEFT. ALL THE WORDS END IN — ACE.

A PAIR	_ _ ACE
TO TRACK DOWN	_ _ ACE
SHAME	_ _ _ _ ACE
SPEED	_ ACE
A TRIBE	_ ACE

Answers:—
Brace, trace, disgrace, pace and race.

SPOT THE ODD-WHIZZ-OUT!

Answer:— ε

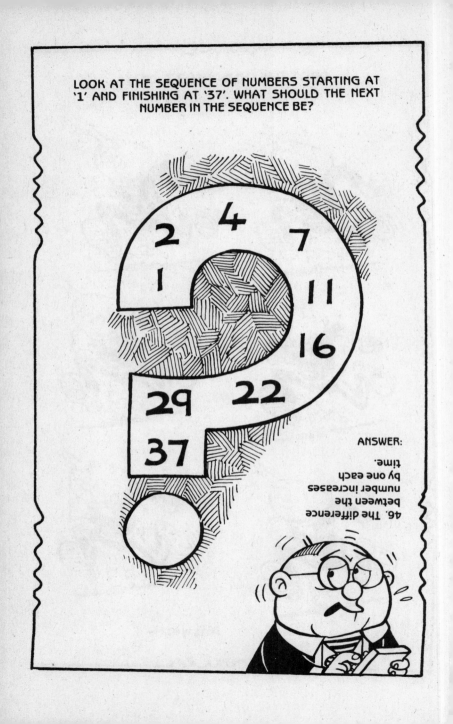